Hairy Bear

Written by Alison Hawes

Illustrated by Mik Brown

Every year, hairy bears from everywhere
meet up with their friends at the Hairy
Bears' Funfair.

Hairy bears from the northern hemisphere get up in the night to prepare for the fair.

They set out cheerfully in the cold night air.

4

The grizzly bears prepare by checking their map.

They travel as quickly as they dare and tear down the road to the Hairy Bears' Funfair.

Grizzly bears travel by road, but brown bears travel to the fair by air.

These bears steer with care as they get near to the funfair!

Brown bears travel by air, but pandas get to the fair by sea. They steer their boats with care through the waves.

Soon all the hairy bears are at the funfair.

Then a little bear appears.
The hairy bears rub their eyes!
"This little bear has no hair," they say.
"This little bear is bare!"

"Oh dear! We fear you cannot come in here," the hairy bears sneer.
"This funfair is only for hairy bears!"

But the little teddy bear is not afraid of the big hairy bears. "That is not fair!" he yells.

"I may be old and have lost my hair.
I may have holes and tears in my fur,
but I am still a bear!" he says.

The hairy bears say they are sorry.
"We have been unfair," they say.

"We do not care if you have lost your hair," say the hairy bears. "Let us all be friends and have fun at the fair!"